COMPACTS are very different from every other type of adventure game book. They have been specially designed so that their play is as convenient as possible.

The special fold-out flap at the front of the book has all your *game accessories*. Within the fold-out flap at the back are all your *score cards*. This means that whenever you have to amend your score card, it can always be located immediately.

The only thing you have to provide yourself is a pen or pencil. You don't even need an eraser because there are enough score cards (a whole 24!) to allow for a fresh one to be used for each new game.

COMPACTS are ideal for playing at home, on holiday, in the car . . . wherever you like!

STEPHEN THRAVES
COMPACT
ADVENTURE GAME BOOKS

CUP HEROES

GREG HILL

Illustrated by Peter Dennis

HODDER AND STOUGHTON
LONDON SYDNEY AUCKLAND

British Library Cataloguing in Publication Data

A catalogue record for this book is available from the British Library

ISBN 0 340 60679 7

Text copyright © Stephen Thraves 1994
Concept copyright © Stephen Thraves 1993
Format copyright © Stephen Thraves 1993
Illustrations copyright © Peter Dennis 1994

First published 1994

Published by Hodder and Stoughton Children's Books,
a division of Hodder Headline plc,
338 Euston Road, London NW1 3BH

Photoset by Hewer Text Composition Services, Edinburgh

Printed and bound in Great Britain by
BPC Hazell Books Ltd
A member of
The British Printing Company Ltd

⚽ THE DREAM STARTS ... ⚽

Only four and a half minutes to go now. You keep anxiously glancing up at the little ramshackle stand to your left to peer at the old clock there. Only four and a half minutes ... and then your very next Cup match could well be under a massive *electronic* scoreboard. In one of the plushest grounds in the country!

But you mustn't get carried away. Your team must hold on to this narrow 1–0 lead first. One silly mistake, one cruel deflection, and all your dreams could crumble to nothing. Who would be a football manager? Especially a *player*-manager like yourself. And especially one in an impoverished non-league team like yours!

Again, you tensely glance up at that antiquated clock. The hands hardly seem to be moving. There are still a good three minutes left. And the opposition are absolutely besieging your goal now, launching one attack after another. You knew it was always going to happen, of course. A league team – even one as lowly as your opposition – was hardly going to let itself be knocked out of the Cup without a fight.

Just over two minutes to go now – and your partner central defender, Darren Palmer, has mercifully just booted the ball well out of danger into touch. Is your team going to do it? Is it going to add the scalp of this *league* team to that of those non-leaguers it has already beaten in the previous preliminary and qualifying rounds?

Not yet! For the opposition's throw was taken very

quickly and once again the ball is bobbing about dangerously in your penalty area. Your heart stops as the ball runs into a little space and one of their forwards unleashes his foot at it. What a brilliant save! Your goalie has surely just taken you through to the next round!

Still forty-five seconds to go, though – and the referee insists that your goalie hurls the ball out immediately. He won't have any time-wasting. That's a terrible clearance. Your goalie's thrown it straight at one of their forwards! *He's offside* you shout as the forward hares into the penalty box. But the linesman's flag remains down. You close your eyes, unable to watch . . .

You hear a loud cheer. They must have scored. No, the cheer was from your passionate little throng of fans. Your goalie must have saved the ball again! Your eyes open to see the ball safely in his hands. Now *please* do a proper clearance this time. He has! The ball's three-quarters of the way down the pitch!

The ninety minutes are up at last – but how much injury time will the referee allow? There surely can't be much. There were hardly any stoppages at all in the second half. But the clock slowly records one minute of injury time, then two. This is absolutely agonising! *Whistle!* you scream inside as the opposition's forward line again sweeps down on your goalie. *WHISTLE!*

Suddenly the whistle's blown. A moment of pure silence seems to follow the shrill sound as you clamp your hands over your eyes. Then everything in this little ground erupts. You hear your fans' ecstatic roar from the tiny 'home' stand and you feel delighted team-mate after delighted team-mate leap on top of you. You've actually done it! You're in the third round of the Cup – the round where the top league clubs enter the competition!

As you return, exhausted, to your team's dressing-room, your mind's a complete blur. One dream seems to be piling up on another. You might be drawn to play against one of the country's *super* teams next – in front of the television cameras and thousands of spectators! And just say you miraculously win that match? Your team could go down as one of the great giant-killers!

And what if you advance even further than that – into the fourth and fifth rounds, and then the quarter-finals? It will mean that you'll have progressed further than any other amateur team in the Cup's whole history!

Your dreams are quite fantastic now. Could your little team do the impossible? Could it battle its way even further *still* – through the semifinals to book a place in the final itself? Could your players be running out of that world-famous tunnel and playing on that legendary turf?

And could they actually be victorious on that turf?

No, surely not. Your dreams are quite absurd. But, as you're the last to enter the dressing-room, you are immediately enveloped by the great spirit and excitement in there and the dreams start again. Perhaps they *could* just come true . . .

⚽ GAME INSTRUCTIONS ⚽

Score Cards

1. For each attempt at the game, you must use one of the 24 score cards contained within the fold-out flap at the *back* of the book.

2. The first column of this score card shows the various rounds of the Cup competition – third, fourth, fifth, quarter-final, semifinal and final. The two boxes to the right of each round are to record the final score for that particular match. The first box is to record YOUR score and the second the OPPOSITION'S score.

3. The game starts with you playing your *third round* match. Every time you score a goal, use a pen or pencil to mark a small **1** to the left of your score box. Every time your opponent scores a goal, mark a small **1** to the right of their score box.

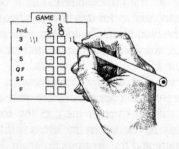

4. When the match has finished, add up the number of goals marked for your side and enter the total in

your score box. Do the same for your opponent. If this final score shows you have won the match, you'll be allowed to continue into the next round of the competition. You then use the score boxes in the same way for the fourth round and, if you win that match, for the fifth round . . . and so on.

5. If you win every round down to and including the final, then you have won the Cup!

6. If you draw a match in any round you must replay it before advancing into the next round (the book will instruct you how). If you lose a match, then you are unfortunately out of the Cup. If you would like another attempt at winning it, you must start the game again right from the beginning (using a fresh score card).

Accessories

7. The accessories for this book are two *lists of draw numbers* (one English, one Scottish) and a grid of *goal action frames*. These accessories are pictured on the fold-out flap at the *front*.

8. The *lists of draw numbers* are for when you have to draw for your opponent before each round of the Cup. If you wish to play in the English Cup, always use the list on the left, and if the Scottish Cup, the list on the right.

9. Whenever you have to make a draw, the book will tell you to pick from a short series of draw numbers.

⚽ GAME INSTRUCTIONS ⚽

You check the number you have chosen against the draw list to find out which team you will play.

10. The teams are colour-coded according to their toughness in Cup competitions. A red team is *VERY TOUGH*, a blue team *TOUGH*, a green team *AVERAGE* and a yellow team *WEAK*. You'll need to remember your opponent's colour code during the course of your match against them. If you forget it, you can always look it up again on the draw list. But what you mustn't do is forget the team name as well. Always be sure to remember it until the draw is made for your next opponent.

11. The *goal action frames* are for when you or your opponent are given a goal-scoring chance during the match. The paragraph instruction will tell you to pick from a list of *goal action frame* grid numbers (e.g. C4, A2, E5). You then simply turn to the front flap to see if that particular frame shows a goal being scored. (There will be a RED CORNER in the bottom left of the frame.) All other frames show either that the scoring chance was wasted – or that the goal was disallowed by the linesman.

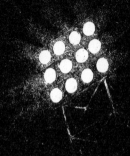

You are now ready to begin
your challenge for the Cup.
Turn the page . . .

1

This afternoon's training session has been a complete fiasco. Every player's mind is on the draw for the Cup's third round at four o'clock! Just think about it . . . there's a strong possibility of playing against a mighty *Premier League* team, full of household names and internationals! But maybe it would be better if you were drawn against a more modest team in this early round; one of the other few minnows still left in the competition. After all, the weaker the opposition the more likely you are to advance to subsequent rounds. You really can't quite decide what type of team you would prefer! But it will very soon be academic, for the draw is now just about to be announced on your radio . . .

To find out who you're playing against in the third round, pick one of these draw numbers: **5** **19** **20** **25** **7** **12** *and then look up that number in the DRAW LIST on the front flap of the book. Be sure to remember this team's name! Now go to 208.*

2

You slap poor Tim on the back in commiseration. How terribly unlucky he was! That was a brilliant shot of his – but the save was even better. Never mind, at least Tim's causing problems for the opposition. It was certainly the right decision to bring him on. *Go to 193*.

3

Your goalkeeper hadn't a chance. What a bad goal to give away. All your players drop their heads in disbelief. If only they hadn't moved so far forward! It's going to be very difficult to lift your players' spirits after this.

Record the opposition's goal on your SCORE CARD. Go next to 133.

4

The crosses are still raining in and your forwards are now in the penalty area helping out. You're not too sure that this is a good idea. Forwards often make bad defenders. And suddenly there's proof of this: a dangerous cross from the left is only half-cleared by one of your forwards and falls nicely for an opposition player. Desperately, your forward tries to make amends and attempts a tackle. But he's much too late and the opposition player is left sprawling on the ground. The cheers are deafening as the referee points to the spot. It's a penalty!

Choose a frame number from the appropriate list below and see whether the opposition score or not:

If they're a RED team	F5	C6	F2
If they're a BLUE team	C4	A1	F6
If they're GREEN team	E1	B6	C3
If they're a YELLOW team	B4	F1	A1

If they score, go to 196. If they don't, go to 105.

5

Since that victory in the last round you've become overnight celebrities! It still has to sink in properly when the time comes for the next round draw. You know that, whichever team you're drawn against, it's going to be very tough now. But after that last game you feel as if you don't really fear anyone! You and your players all sit round the radio, tensely listening to the draw. Your number comes out first – it's a home game! But who's the opposition?

To find out, pick one of these draw numbers: ❸ ❶ ⑮ ⑱ ❷ *and then look up that number in the DRAW LIST on the front flap of the book. Be sure to remember this team's name. Now go to 142.*

6

Well, it's now a corner for their team instead of for yours – but at least your keeper's fast back-pedal and brilliant tip-over mean that you weren't punished more severely. Not for the moment, at any rate! But their corner-kick is as careless as yours. And a championship side should know a lot better! *Go to 146.*

7

One goal up already! Andy's chip was so precise, their goalie barely stood a chance!

Record your team's goal on your SCORE CARD. Go next to 22.

8

You simply can't believe it. How on earth did their goalie get his hands to that one? He didn't even have to palm it away for a corner but neatly caught it. A bitter disappointment – and only five minutes left now! ***Go next to 72.***

9

Now Dean Walsh is up front, giving their defenders someone else to mark, your forwards have a little more space. A hopeful ball out of defence finds an unmarked Scott Baker on the wing. He sweeps the ball forward and gets in his first cross for ages! Big Andy Jones is the first to react in the muddy conditions. His firm header down is perfectly aimed at Dean. Before a tackle comes in, Dean hits a glorious first-time half-volley . . .

Choose a frame number from the appropriate list below and see whether you score or not:

If playing RED team	B1	E5	C2
If playing BLUE team	E1	A4	C5
If playing GREEN team	F5	B3	E5
If playing YELLOW team	B4	C2	A4

If you do score, go to 197. If you don't, go to 58.

10

Your team is in despair. You're out! All you as manager can do is slap each of your lads on the back and murmur 'Well done'. The lap of honour is an effort but it's something you feel your team owes itself. Even getting this far has been a considerable achievement!

If you would like to compete for the Cup again, you must return to the start of its

third round at Paragraph 1. With the experi-
ence you've gained, and perhaps with just a
little more luck, you might go even further
next time!

11

All your players mob Scott for putting in such a great cross. Although it was technically an own goal, it was *his* really! This late lead for your side whips up a real hornets' nest, however; the opposition launching one frantic attack after another. The next five minutes seem like five hours! But somehow your tired players survive the onslaught. The whistle is finally blown, its shrill sound music to your ears! *Go to 47.*

12

Dejectedly, your goalie picks the ball out of the back of the net. What a thunderous volley that was from their striker! At least there's still most of the match left for you to try to pull it back, though.

Record your opponents' goal on your SCORE CARD. Go next to 186.

13

Dean deftly scoops the ball into the air and it's like a cavalry charge as your three tallest players rush in behind the wall to try to meet it with their heads. But they get in each other's way and the ball eludes every one of them, dropping harmlessly into the hands of the opposition's goalie. Perhaps a direct shot at goal would have been a better idea after all! *Go to 206*.

14

Dean is almost in tears. Your most talented player has missed! None of you can bear to watch as the opposition's last penalty-taker steps up to the spot. The mighty roar all round you tells you that the score is now level at 4–4. But your players' confidence has been badly shaken after losing the initiative like this. Your next penalty-taker, Gary Weeks, completely mis-strikes the ball and it balloons over the bar. Again, you can't bear to watch. If the opposition put this next penalty away, the match is theirs. After an eternal silence, three of the four stands in the ground almost have their roofs lifted off. The home fans are delirious. Their team has won! *Go to 170*.

15

Your poor goalie didn't really stand a chance. That was a terrible deflection for him to try to read. It might even have come off *you*. If you lose this final as a result of that goal, you're going to be haunted by that possibility for the rest of your life!

Record your opponents' goal on your SCORE CARD. Go next to 207.

16

Although you're disappointed with a draw, when it finally sinks in, you realise that it was probably a fair result. And, of course, the replay is on *your* ground! For the first ninety minutes of this Tuesday-evening match there's barely a chance at either end. However, extra time is a completely different story. Dean hits the bar with a twenty-yarder and the opposition have two great shots saved and then one kicked off the line! Just as it's looking as if the game will drift towards penalties, one of their defenders passes back to his goalkeeper. Knowing that the keeper isn't allowed to pick the ball up, Andy Jones races in and blocks it as he tries to kick it clear. He then coolly chips the ball over the goalie's head . . .

Choose a frame number from the appropriate list below and see whether Andy scores:

If playing RED team	C5	F3	B2
If playing BLUE team	D5	E1	C2
If playing GREEN team	F3	B4	F5

If Andy does score, go to 160. If he doesn't, go to 205.

17

Any second now, television will be showing the draw for the semifinals. With only four teams left in the competition it shouldn't take very long! The draw will be as tense as ever for you, though. The other three teams are all first-rate sides but one of them has not been playing quite as well this season as they normally do. It's that slightly off-form team that you're praying for! The glory of playing the likely league champions can wait for the final. All you want to do now is *reach* that final!

To find out your semifinal opponents, pick one of these draw numbers: ❿ ❽ ⓱ *and then look up that number in the DRAW LIST on the front flap of the book. Be sure to remember this team's name! Now go to 107.*

18

Well, league players aren't going to miss chances like that. Their number eight put it away so coolly. This long-ball tactic of yours was obviously a big mistake!

Record your opponents' goal on your SCORE CARD. Go next to 21.

Although you've got their forwards tightly marked, their defenders are now able to move up to the halfway line to support their midfield. Suddenly all the play seems to be in your own half. It's not long before the inevitable happens. Your other central defender manages only a desperate half clearance and the ball runs to their number six just outside your penalty area. He volleys it first time towards the top corner of your goal . . .

Choose a frame number from the appropriate list below and see whether your opponents score or not:

If they're a RED team	D6	E6	F5
If they're a BLUE team	E1	D2	D4
If they're a GREEN team	D2	A2	E6

If your opponents score, go to 60. If they don't, go to 138.

It was a great tip over the bar from your goalie – but he had to give away a corner and so the danger isn't over yet. But at least poor old Duncan doesn't have to mark those two giants on his own this time! You quickly beckon back the rest of your tall players into the box. As it turns out, it's YOU who leaps to the in-swinger first. You coolly nod it back to the grateful arms of your goalie. *Go to 62.*

21

Only twenty minutes of the match left now and you decide it's time to get Dean Walsh to take some of the long throw-ins he is so famous for. They are only likely to produce results, though, if Andy Jones is assisted by another big lad in the goalmouth. Do you push up Darren Palmer, your partner central defender, or your young full back? Darren would probably be more effective alongside Andy, but it would mean that you would then have to protect the centre of the defence on your own! Is it a risk you dare take?

If push up Darren   go to 66
If push up full back   go to 158

22

As the game approaches the twenty-minute mark, you seem to be matching your superior opposition in every department. Except on one of the wings. If that tricky left-winger of theirs isn't controlled soon, he's likely to win the match on his own. Your full back is having a terrible time with him! You must instruct another player to give him some assistance. Should you move one of your other defenders across – or get your own winger, Scott Baker, to drop back a little?

If move defender across **go to 180**
If drop back winger **go to 111**

23

Everything now looks very hopeful. A great goal – and the opposition just don't seem to know how to deal with you! One or two of their players look towards their manager in his dugout. Thankfully, he doesn't seem to have any answers either!

Record your team's goal on your SCORE CARD. Go next to 210.

24

The fact that you are now one man down really motivates the opposition. They suddenly go all-out for goal! There's a moment of relief from the constant pressure, though, as your partner central defender frantically boots the ball right upfield. You don't care where it goes as long as it's well out of the danger area! The ball rather luckily drops down near Andy, though. He leaps high into the air, outjumping their central defender, and nods the ball towards Scott. Your young winger has only one defender to beat. The opposition had pushed up far too much! Scott neatly evades this desperate defender, carries the ball another yard or two, and then unleashes a fierce shot . . .

Choose a frame number from the appropriate list below and see whether Scott scores:
>   *If playing RED team*   C6   F1   A5
>   *If playing BLUE team*   A2   C3   B6
>   *If playing GREEN team*   C4   F2   D6
If Scott does score, go to 183. If not, go to 110.

25
There's total disbelief all round the ground after Dean's goal – from all except your faithful band of supporters, that is. Surely your team can't possibly go even further in the Cup, the opposition fans seem to be thinking. Surely you're not going to put out this team as well . . . one of the finest in the land!

Record your team's goal on your SCORE CARD. Go next to 103.

To try to set an example, you take the very first penalty yourself. You smash it just inside the left upright! Your supporters roar with delight – but then there's an even bigger roar from them. The opposition *MISS* their first penalty! You wonder whether being at home is actually a disadvantage when it comes to the tension of sudden death. Nevertheless, they put their next three penalties skilfully away. So, fortunately, does your team. The score is now 4–3 in your favour. And if Dean Walsh scores from this last penalty, the opposition can't catch up!

Choose a frame number from the appropriate list below and see whether Dean scores:

If playing RED team   E3   B2   A3
If playing BLUE team   D5   C1   D6
If playing GREEN team   A2   D3   B5

If Dean does score, go to 67. If he doesn't, go to 14.

The deafening sound confirms it. While you and your other defenders are still racing towards him, their striker has obviously found the back of your net. What a stupid goal to give away!

Record your opponents' goal on your SCORE CARD. Go next to 198.

When Scott begins his surges down the left wing your opponents are taken completely by surprise. They can't decide who should mark him! Before they have a chance to sort themselves out, Scott is racing clear. He nips to the goal line and then cuts the ball back for Dean who controls it and then chips it deftly goalwards . . .

Choose a frame number from the appropriate list below and see whether Dean scores or not:

    If playing RED team   *C3*   *B4*   *C6*
    If playing BLUE team   *F5*   *C2*   *A1*
    If playing GREEN team   *C6*   *B3*   *E1*
If he does score, go to 141. If not, go to 113.

29

Both teams are taking a long time to settle down. Even the opposition – the league champions and with six internationals in their side – are playing very nervously. Their midfield is particularly tentative and, with three of your players tightly marking in this department, they've been able to create very little so far. The only attempts at goal have been a couple of extremely hopeful long-range shots. They barely test your keeper. It's still early days yet – but so far so good! *Go to 114.*

30

Neither your left-back nor the rest of your players can believe it. And, judging by the momentary delay before their delirium breaks out, nor can your fans. You've actually put the ball in the net in the Cup Final!

Record your team's goal on your SCORE CARD. Go next to 146.

31

After the excitement of the penalty, the remainder of the first half is all rather low key. This uninspired patch continues into the first ten minutes or so of the second half. But then your opponents really start to apply the pressure again. Only good defending is keeping them out! Your right-back is left with a badly-turned ankle after one of these interceptions, however, and he needs several minutes' treatment. Although he's finally on his feet again – and insists he's fit enough to carry on – you notice he's still hobbling quite badly. You've got a tough but important decision to make. Do you allow him to continue with this injury . . . or bring on a substitute for him?

If leave him on**   **go to 144
If substitute**   **go to 179

32

That has to be one of the best goals this national stadium has ever seen! Your fans certainly think it was. They're going absolutely wild in their stand. Whether you eventually win this final or not, it's most memorable moment will always belong to your little non-league side!

Record your team's goal on your SCORE CARD. Go next to 207.

33

Since their substitution your opponents are trying to get as many high balls into your area as possible. Fortunately, you've now got enough height in your defence to cope. One of those high crosses is headed out by Andy to Duncan. Your number four controls the ball and then carries it upfield. The break is on! By the time a defender comes to tackle him, Duncan is already across the halfway line. He plays the ball to Scott who is running through like a train. Just as Scott is about to be tackled, he lets fly at goal . . .

Choose a frame number from the appropriate list below and see whether Scott scores:
  If playing RED team   E1   B6   C4
  If playing BLUE team   F2   C4   F1
  If playing GREEN team   A5   F1   B4
If Scott does score, go to 163. If he doesn't, go to 96.

34

It looks as if you chose the correct tactic for this early part of the match. Although your players start the match very nervously, this containing game gradually seems to build their confidence. Proudly, you urge them on from their centre as they frustrate one attack after another. You've comfortably survived a whole five minutes now! *Go to 112.*

35

The complete silence all round you is absolute music to your ears. You've scored! Your first goal *ever* against league opposition. And how calmly Andy put it away! Anyone would think he had been playing against league opposition every week! You must ensure that your players don't get carried away by the goal, though. The match still has a long way to go!

Record your goal on your SCORE CARD. Go next to 133.

36

The noise of the ball smacking the woodwork can be heard all round the ground. Matt Coles stares up at the sky in disbelief. Fortunately *you* keep your eyes firmly on the ball, which is still in play and spinning furiously as it drops from the sky. Their goalkeeper is not sure where it is. Here's a second chance for your team! You hurl yourself towards the descending ball . . .

Choose a frame number from the appropriate list below and see whether you score:

If playing RED team	*D5*	*C6*	*E1*
If playing BLUE team	*A2*	*F3*	*D6*
If playing GREEN team	*F5*	*E3*	*A1*
If playing YELLOW team	*B2*	*D6*	*B4*

If you do score, go to 68. If you don't, go to 185.

The ground echoes with your fans' deep groans. Your goalie showed great reflexes in almost getting his fingertips to the ball, but really he saw it far too late to stand a decent chance!

Record your opponents' goal on your SCORE CARD. Go next to 127.

With your left-back moved to sweeper, the opposition are now finding so much space in that area of the pitch. Their winger suddenly makes a run to the goal line. He sends over a pinpoint cross to his tall striker. The striker's header is looped cleverly towards the top corner of your goal . . .

Choose a frame number from the appropriate list below and see whether your opponents score or not:

    If they're a RED team   *B4*   *A6*   *C5*
    If they're a BLUE team   *D1*   *E6*   *B3*
If they do score, go to 187. If not, go to 121.

That must go down as the miss of the match! How lucky you were! You simply can't allow them so much possession in future. *Go to 21.*

40

Defeat at this stage – so near but yet so far – is absolutely heart-breaking. You're lifted a little, though, by the tremendous applause for your team. It's coming from all round the ground; every single supporter – yours and theirs – on their feet. It's been an incredible achievement for an amateur team to get this far in the Cup; the furthest in the history of the competition. But your opponents were one giant-killing act too many. They were just a bit *too* good for you. As your lads finally and tearfully leave the pitch, you proudly go from one to the other, assuring them all that they'll be back!

If you would like to compete for the Cup again, you must return to the start of the third round at Paragraph 1. With the experience you've gained, and perhaps with a little more luck, you might go all the way next time!

41

Andy's put it away! He placed the ball brilliantly out of their goalkeeper's reach to give him no chance!

Record your team's goal on your SCORE CARD. Go next to 198.

42

What a great shame Andy's header was straight at the keeper. That was the move of the match. If his header had been directed a little more to the right, it would surely also have been the *goal* of the match! *Go to 54.*

43

The match is now some ten minutes into the second half and Dean seems to be coping with their creative star very well. But Dean is *your* most creative player and you're badly missing those lovely balls he plays out to Scott and Gary on the wings. This allows the opposition's other midfielders considerably more of the ball. One weaving run from their number seven takes him right to the edge of your area. He slips the ball to his striker, who unleashes an absolute thunderbolt . . .

Choose a frame number from the appropriate list below and see whether your opponents score or not:
    If they're a RED team   *F2   E3   C6*
    If they're a BLUE team   *A1   A5   D6*
If your opponents do score, go to 188. If they don't, go to 71.

44
Your keeper disconsolately picks the ball out of the back of the net. He had absolutely no chance with that point-blank header. What a disaster; giving away a goal this late on in the match. And it's YOUR fault. You should have organised a much better marking job on that substitute!

Record your opponents' goal on your SCORE CARD. Go next to 62.

45
When half-time arrives, you ponder your tactics for the second part of the game. Ideally, you would like to push both your full backs forward to support your wingers. But you are playing well-coached professionals here –

you've got to be careful! Nevertheless, you feel you must be positive, resolving to push up *one* of your backs at any rate. Which should it be?

If right-back   go to 75
If left-back   go to 125

46

Aware that this free kick is a great chance for them, you consider how you should construct your defensive wall. Do you just put in as many players as possible? Or do you put only, say, three men into the wall? This will give your goalie a better sight of the ball and allow your other defenders to mark for a cross.

If large wall   go to 165
If small wall   go to 88

47

Even the policemen, the ambulance service, the photographers, the officials, the reporters – and yes, even your opponents' fans – are on their feet clapping. A microphone is thrust into your face and the television commentator asks how you feel about taking a non-league side all the way to the Cup Final – for the first time ever! You're unable to give him an answer. It's going to be a long while yet before you can believe it. Surely this is all just some crazy dream! *Go to 182*.

48

The opposition are quite livid with themselves, every-one blaming everyone else for the goal. They know that a team of top professionals should never have slipped into such complacency like that. There was always going to be the risk of being caught! They desperately try to make up for their error but it's all just too frantic. They can't beat the final whistle! *Go to 171*.

49

This is devastating – a goal so close to half-time! And you feel it was all your fault too. Your instructions all but rooted your poor keeper to the spot!

***Record your opponents' goal on your SCORE CARD. Go next to 31*.**

50

There are now only twenty minutes to go. The midfield of both teams seem to be dominating and the game is getting a little scrappy. One or two of the younger players are tiring. Scott Baker has given everything. A fresh pair of legs could make all the difference now. But should you bring on your midfield substitute or your forward substitute and go all out for a goal in the last twenty minutes?

Bring on forward **go to 106**
Bring on midfield **go to 83**

51

Your fans let out huge sighs of relief as the ball bounces back off the post towards Dean Walsh and he quickly punts it upfield. The ball, in fact, crosses the touchline. This is what you were hoping for. The break in play gives you a chance to replace your injured right-back with a substitute. It's something you really should have done several minutes ago! *Go to 118*.

52

As you do your warm-up exercises on the pitch, you wonder whether you have chosen the *right* tactic for the early part of the game. You're soon going to find out, because the referee now blows his whistle to start the match. You have never seen your players look so nervous! You hope these nerves will quickly subside once the game is under way. But from their very first touch it's one bad pass after another! They also quickly lose their shape. When you told them to go for all-out attack, you didn't mean the whole team! The defence is pressing much too far upfield – and, suddenly, they pay the penalty for this. One of the opposition's forwards finds himself with a clear run on your goal . . .

Choose a frame number from the appropriate list below and check on the front flap to see whether the opposition score or not:

If they're a RED team	F2	E3	D4
If they're a BLUE team	A6	F6	D2
If they're a GREEN team	D1	E6	A2
If they're a YELLOW team	A5	F4	E6

If the opposition do score, go to 129. If they don't, go to 80.

53

The free kick was easily cleared to the halfway line by the opposition's tall central defender. Darren Palmer heads it back as defenders continue to dominate. For the last twenty minutes there have been few chances at either end. No one wants to give anything away. It will be half-time soon which will give everyone time to catch breath. *Go to 192.*

When half-time arrives, you work really hard at motivating your players. This team can definitely be beaten! Your pep talk seems to have immediate effect. Your players pour forward at the start of the second half. On the right wing, young Scott Baker runs at a loose clearance and then responds to the crowd's screams to go it alone. He easily glides past one defender, then two ... but the third brings him down. Despite your fans' howls for a penalty, the referee insists the foul was just outside the area and awards a free kick. Dean Walsh will of course take it but he glances towards you, the manager, for guidance. Do you secretly instruct him to *float* the ball – so a team-mate can with luck pick it up on the other side of the opponents' wall – or to take a direct shot at goal?

> **If float ball**   **go to 13**
> **If take direct shot**   **go to 84**

55

Your main worry at half-time is how to nullify your opponents' £4 million-rated number eight. With his clever little runs and marvellous passing skills, he's completely dictating the game. The truth is that *none* of your players is anywhere near good enough to mark him comprehensively. But one of you is going to have to make an attempt at it or you'll be hammered. Should you ask Dean Walsh to try to control him? Or should you do the job yourself?

> **If prefer Dean**   **go to 43**
> **If prefer yourself** **go to 139**

56

What a great save that was! Andy's chip was excellent, but their goalkeeper, leaping backwards in the mud like a ballet dancer, just managed to tip it over! ***Go to 22.***

57

The silence from three sides of the ground and the cheers of your supporters behind the goal tells you that Craig has done it! Now the pressure is back on the opposition. Your goalkeeper doesn't even have to save their next penalty shot. It goes way over the bar and into the stand! Now – *can you steal the glory?* For the next penalty shot is *yours*. And it's not a penalty to save the match any more, but *to win it!* It all happens so quickly. You hardly think about it; you hit the ball as hard and low as you can. It thumps into the back of the net! *Go to 73*.

58

Dean punches the air after bursting the back of the net. He still hasn't noticed the linesman's flag. Your fans have, though, for their cheering abruptly subsides. The linesman must have thought Dean was a fraction offside! *Go to 203*.

59

That brilliant save from their goalie seems to inspire the opposition. There's now one onslaught after another on your goal. One tremendous shot is only just fisted away by your keeper. It bobbles in the penalty area, your left-back having to race both their strikers for it. He's just ahead of them – but then his legs suddenly give way with cramp. The next thing you know, the ball is in the back of your net. They've scored in the dying seconds. There's no way back now. *Go to 40*.

60

What a tremendous shot! Even though your keeper got his fingertips to it, there was nothing he could do to stop it going in. There was too much power behind it!

Record your opponents' goal on your SCORE CARD. Go next to 45.

61

As the match progresses the rain falls harder and harder. Your defenders play on terrible surfaces week in and week out, of course, but this is bad even for them! The opposition have started well. They're making the ball do the work. There's no need to turn quickly when the passing is this good! But then a through-ball to their forwards is hit far too hard. It will run to your goalie. No, it won't – for it suddenly stops dead in the thick mud. One of their strikers is quickly on to it and hits it first time . . .

Choose a frame number from the appropriate

list below and see whether the opposition score or not:

If they're a RED team	F6	C3	E4
If they're a BLUE team	D4	F2	C1
If they're a GREEN team	D3	E6	A1
If they're a YELLOW team	D2	C6	A5

If they do score, go to 85. If not, go to 132.

62

There are only a few minutes of the match left now. But once again, the opposition lobs the ball high into your area. Your keeper punches it clear but back it comes again. You're battling frantically to keep it out when suddenly the final whistle is blown. It's the end of the biggest game your tiny ground has ever seen!

Turn to your SCORE CARD and tot up the final score for this quarter-final match. If you won it, go to 67. If you drew it, go to 119. If you lost it, go to 170.

63

It seems that your opponents have watched some of Scott's performances in the earlier rounds of the Cup. They're completely stifling the service to your right wing! Perhaps if you had switched Scott to the left wing, you could have taken them by surprise. Well, you persevere with the way things are for the moment. But if you don't make some sort of breakthrough soon, you're going to have to come up with some new ideas! *Go to 172.*

64
You tell your players to relax and enjoy themselves but, as the referee tosses his coin, you notice that you're trembling a fair amount yourself. The ref informs you that you have won the toss and asks which way you want to play. There's a lot of wind this afternoon. This is likely to play a big part in the match. So should you choose the advantage of the wind behind you for the first half or the second?

If first half   go to 134
If second half   go to 164

65
The ball struck the left upright! How desperately unlucky! Dean simply can't believe it, sinking to his knees and hugging his head. You won't get nearer to a goal than that! *Go to 206.*

Dean is taking every single throw-in now and they're almost as good as corners! And the next throw-in you win is in the perfect position – just level with the six-yard line. Dean wipes the mud off the ball and takes aim. The massive throw floats right into the goalmouth. Darren Palmer leaps above the crowd of players round him and flicks the ball at just the right height for big Andy. With a fierce nod of the head, Andy directs it goalwards . . .

Choose a frame number from the appropriate list below and see whether you score:

If playing RED team	D3	A1	C6
If playing BLUE team	C1	C3	E4
If playing GREEN team	D3	E4	A1
If playing YELLOW team	C3	E4	C1

If you do score, go to 199. If you don't, go to 8.

67

It's quite impossible to believe. You're the player-manager of a side who has just reached the semifinals of the Cup! Ecstatic fans are congratulating you as you do your lap of honour. You have to pinch yourself to make sure you aren't dreaming. You'll probably only be absolutely convinced when you see it in tomorrow's papers! *Go next to 17.*

68

Your players delightedly clamour round you after this clinically-taken goal. But you cut short their celebrations and order your team to get back to their positions for the restart. There's now likely to be some fierce defending to do!

Add a goal for your team on your SCORE CARD. Go next to 50.

69

Your ten men are still holding out superbly. Then the referee blows for a penalty against your right-back. No, he must be kidding! That was a perfectly good tackle from him! You then let out a huge sigh of relief. It wasn't a penalty the ref had blown for – but full time. The match is over!

Turn to your SCORE CARD and tot up the final

score for this fifth-round match. If you have won it, go to 90. If you have drawn it, go to 16. If you have lost it, go to 128.

70

Your opponents may have four men up front now but there's no one to give them the right pass. You keep cutting it out! Indeed, you're starting to create a few chances of your own now. A lovely ball suddenly puts Scott Baker through. He pretends to cut inside to shoot but then suddenly takes the ball round the *outside* of the defender. With the next defender, he swerves on the inside – but he's caught in full flight by the opponent's outstretched leg. The referee has no hesitation in awarding a penalty! Dean Walsh places the ball on the spot, takes a deep breath, and strikes it towards goal . . .

Choose a frame number from the appropriate list below and see whether you score:

If playing RED team	*B4*	*C4*	*A1*
If playing BLUE team	*F5*	*A2*	*F1*
If playing GREEN team	*C6*	*E1*	*D6*

If you score, go to 109. If you don't, go to 204.

71

What a great save. Your goalie even managed to hold on to it. You can't rely on him to keep performing those miracles, though. You've got to start attacking more and take some of the pressure off your beleaguered goalmouth. *Go to 210.*

72

There are only seconds left of the match now. Your fans chant their support as they wait for the referee to blow his whistle. All through the match they have been determined to enjoy themselves! The whistle can only just be heard above the noise. It's all over!

Turn to your SCORE CARD and tot up the final score for this fourth-round match. If you have won it, go to 124. If you have drawn it, go to 201. If you have lost it, go to 10.

73

Even in your wildest dreams you never thought it was possible. You've actually knocked out this league team! Your players all race over to your little band of fans to celebrate. Haven't those fans been fantastic, too! You could never have done it without them. You must stop your players throwing their shirts to them, though. You need them for the next round! *Go next to 5*.

74

Dean covers his eyes, then drops to his knees. That crossbar could well be the difference between you making the final and going out. He knows that he probably should have trapped the ball and taken his time over the shot. This wasn't the time to be spectacular! *Go to 103*.

75

Not long into the second half, your right-back makes his first tentative run at the opposition. He takes the ball as far as he can down the wing and then, just before he's tackled, quickly sends a low, hard cross into the penalty area. Whether he intended this or not, the ball goes straight through all their defenders to find big Andy

Jones at the far post. The angle is tight, but it's an excellent chance . . .

Choose a frame number from the appropriate list below and see whether Andy scores or not:

If playing RED team	*A4*	*D3*	*E5*
If playing BLUE team	*E1*	*E4*	*A4*
If playing GREEN team	*B4*	*C1*	*B1*

If Andy does score, go to 41. If not, go to 161.

76

Your opponents' fans are going wild with delight, their stands a sea of waving banners. After an early goal like this, the double is surely in the bag for them now! As for your fans, the whole stand is stunned into complete silence. The dream seems to be rapidly fading already. Goals are difficult enough to create in a Cup Final as it is – without having to score extra ones to cancel out silly mistakes!

Record your opponents' goal on your SCORE CARD. Go next to 114.

77

To your relief, their penalty-taker *does* stroke the ball to his right. Your goalie just gets his fingertips to it and pushes it against the post, then safely smothers the fortunate rebound. As all your players crowd round him, slapping him on the back for this superb save, he winks gratefully towards you. Your gamble was the right one! *Go to 31*.

78

While the opposition's fans are still celebrating their goal, you signal towards one of your substitutes on the bench. He's to replace your injured right-back straight away! Of course, this substitution should have been made a minute or two ago. Instead of being kind to your defender by leaving him on, you have simply made him feel completely responsible for the goal. If you go on to lose the match, he'll think it's all his fault! *Go to 118*.

79

Andy is certainly involved much more now that you're employing this high-ball tactic. He achieves one flick-on after another, outjumping their central defenders every single time! The problem is that there's never anyone near enough to him to take advantage of these flick-ons. This starts to frustrate your big striker and he carelessly heads one of the balls straight to the feet of an opposition defender. This defender quickly feeds the ball forward to his left-winger. A moment later the speedy left-winger centres it towards one of their strikers who hits an excellent half-volley on the turn.

Can your surprised goalie react fast enough to just fingertip it away . . .?

Choose a frame number from the appropriate list below and see whether your opponents score or not:

If they're a RED team	*B3*	*A2*	*C6*
If they're a BLUE team	*C5*	*A1*	*C3*
If they're a GREEN team	*D6*	*C3*	*C6*

If they do score, go to 115. If not, go to 162.

80

What a brilliant fingertip save that was! Your goalie has saved you from absolute disaster. Going 1–0 down at this early stage would have totally dispirited your team. Still, the danger isn't over yet. There's the corner to come from that save. Fortunately, though, it's a bad one, the ball swinging right behind the goal for a goal kick to your side. *Go to 112.*

81

You're coming under more and more pressure from the opposition. You can't say you weren't expecting it, though. They are one of the best teams in the country, after all, and they obviously want to reach the final as much as you do! Just as you're waiting for the half-time whistle to blow so you can rethink your tactics, the referee awards your opponents a free kick for Duncan Hill's wild tackle right at the edge of your penalty area . . . *Go to 46*.

82

You're not too disappointed at the away draw. Your players always seem to raise their game when playing in front of the bigger crowds. But the three-week wait to the match seems longer than ever. You and your players are really suffering from your nerves! At last, however, you're running out on to the superb pitch. While you're warming up for the match, you make a quick survey of your latest opponents. They look good even just kicking the ball about! You particularly study their two best players; the ex-international left-winger

and the record-signing number eight. You must watch
these two carefully, perhaps putting an extra marker on
one of them. You can't put extra markers on *both* or it
will weaken your team too much elsewhere. But which
do you fear most?

If the winger   **go to 202**
If the number eight **go to 120**

83

Your midfield substitute, Greg Atkinson, is your side's
most experienced player. And it soon shows – for he has
a real calming influence on the game. You look far less
likely to concede a goal now. On the other hand, you
don't seem to be creating as many chances since young
Scott went off . . . and it won't be much longer before
the final whistle is blown! ***Go to 193***.

84

You stand alongside Dean so your opponents can't be
sure who's actually to take the free kick. Dean takes a
couple of steps back from the ball. You make him wait a

moment, however, so you can ask the referee to move the opposition's defensive wall a little further back. As soon as the ref has corrected the wall and blown his whistle, you make a dummy run over the ball. Dean follows immediately behind you, curling the ball towards the far left of the line of players. It clears them easily enough but will it also clear the goal?

Choose a frame number from the appropriate list below and see if Dean scores or not:

If playing RED team	*D5*	*C5*	*F3*
If playing BLUE team	*E3*	*C2*	*B2*
If playing GREEN team	*D5*	*B3*	*D6*

If he does score, go to 143. If not, go to 65.

85

Your frustrated goalie hurls a handful of mud to the ground while your opponents dance round him in celebration. It wasn't them that beat him but this awful sticky pitch! There's no point in complaining about it, though. Your team's one down and that's that!

Record the opposition's goal on your SCORE CARD. Go next to 22.

86

It's now time to follow your trembling players out of the luxurious dressing-room and into the tunnel. They intermittently shake their limbs, trying in vain to relax themselves. You gulp as an official instucts you to start leading them out on to the pitch. It's as if you're walking off the end of the earth: there's just a dazzle of bright daylight ahead of you and a strange, expectant silence. Then a deafening roar breaks out all round you. The packed stadium is quite terrifying, a heaving sea of noise and colour . . . *Go to 154*.

87

Your opponents obviously want to score just before half-time themselves! They suddenly turn up the pressure, but Dean ably helps your defenders to stifle the various dangers. As the half-time whistle is blown, you wonder what would have happened if you had pushed Dean forward. Would you have scored that goal . . . or would you perhaps have conceded one instead? *Go next to 203*.

88

Three of the opposition's team stand over the ball, waiting for the referee to whistle for the free kick. The moment he does, one of these players runs to the left over the ball, one runs to the right, and the third gently taps it. The ball has a wicked curve on it and spins some way to the right of your three-man wall. Will your goalie be able to dive across to it in time?

Choose a frame number from the appropriate list below and see whether your opponents score or not:
   If they're a RED team   B4   C3   E1
   If they're a BLUE team   F5   E1   D4
If they do score, go to 147. If not, go to 123.

89

You've played as sweeper before – but not against this level of opposition! Fortunately, your other defenders are marking very tightly, giving you as few anxious moments as possible. You wonder why there's a sudden cheer from your fans. Glancing towards your physio on the touchline, you see that Duncan is ready to come back on. What a relief . . . you can now move back to the position you're comfortable with! *Go to 81.*

90

You can't believe it. You're actually into the quarter-finals! As you run, exhausted, towards your delirious fans, you notice that even the opposition's supporters are applauding your astonishing success as well. All round the ground they are on their feet cheering. Later in the changing-rooms you try to come to terms with it all – *you're through to the Cup's quarter-final! Go to 191.*

91

The opposition are trying to take full advantage of the fact that you are one man down, absolutely besieging your penalty area with cross after cross. With big Andy back to help out, however, you're just about able to cope with these crosses. But Andy is now badly missed up front. With only one striker left there upfield, it's impossible to switch the emphasis to attack. *Go to 69*.

92

Scott's corner-kick is a bad one, far too hurried, and the opposition hook the ball clear to the halfway line. The only players anywhere near it are your left-back and their number seven! Their player is a fraction quicker to the ball and he starts to hare forward with it. All you can do is helplessly watch from this other end of the pitch as the winger suddenly notices your goalie off his line and chips him . . .

Choose a frame number from the list below and see whether your opponents score or not:

A6   C5   E1

If they do score, go to 166. If not, go to 6.

Your fans are going wild. That's probably the best flowing movement ever seen on this little pitch of yours. Andy's run after he flicked the ball into your path must have been a good thirty yards. And didn't he finish it with a great header? Even your distinguished opponents would find it hard to emulate that move!

Record your team's goal on your SCORE CARD. Go next to 54.

94

You don't know how your players are going to survive this extra time. Cramp is rife amongst them now and they're so weary they really don't seem to care any more whether they win or lose! Fortunately, the opposition are equally exhausted and the extra minutes slip undramatically by. Everyone seems to be happy with a replay. But then your side win a freak corner and you urge your players to try to motivate themselves just once more. Why go through all this effort again? In response to your pleas, the corner-kick is struck quickly towards the near post. You meet the ball here yourself, flicking it back towards Duncan Hill. He puts every sinew into a fierce volley . . .

Choose a frame number from the list below to see whether Duncan scores or not:

C5   D2   C3

If Duncan does score, go to 48. If he doesn't, go to 167.

95

It's now deep into the second period of extra time and most of your players can barely move their legs any more. Scott Baker, however, suddenly attempts one last desperate run down his wing. He grits his teeth, absolute agony showing on his face! He somehow makes the goal line and hooks back a thunderous low cross. Andy Jones is simply too tired to meet the ball but it luckily deflects off one of their defenders, spinning towards the goal . . .

Choose a frame number from the appropriate list below and see whether this is a goal for you or not:

    If playing RED team   A5   D2   B6
    If playing BLUE team   D3   F2   E6
If it is, go to 11. If it isn't, go to 59.

That was brilliantly smothered by the goalie! He got his whole body behind the ball, just as the textbooks tell you to do. He did perhaps have some luck, though: Scott's shot bounced just a shade too early, seeming to slow up a little before reaching the goalie. *Go to 62*.

You keep passing the ball out to Scott's wing but he continues to be tightly marked there. He almost manages one run but a good sliding tackle from the opposition leads to an immediate counter-attack. The ball is swiftly taken down to your goal line and then accurately centred. You desperately leap with their tall striker for the ball. Whether it ricochets off your head or his you're not really sure – all that matters is that it's spinning towards the top corner of your net . . .

Choose a frame number from the list below and see whether your opponents score or not:

C2   F4   A2

If they do score, go to 15. If not, go to 152.

98

What a cracking header from Andy! That will certainly settle your nerves. Only ten minutes gone and you're in the lead. But you mustn't for a moment forget that this is one of the best teams in the country you're playing. You're by no means through to the final yet!

Record your team's goal on your SCORE CARD. Go next to 174.

99

Gary sinks to his knees, unable to believe that their goalkeeper was able to smother his shot. The goalie made it look so easy too; that's what's particularly dispiriting. A shot obviously has to be quite exceptional to beat keepers of this calibre. *Go to 210.*

100

How close that was to what a few months ago would have been the unthinkable; your team scoring a goal in the Cup Final! Their keeper only just saw the ball in time. You only hope that this isn't your best chance for that historic goal gone! *Go to 146.*

101

Scott's first two attempts leave him lying in the mud after excellent tackles. Then, suddenly, after a glorious pass from your midfield, he's flying down the wing in much more space and all your team is racing forward hoping for a good cross. But once again the full back times his tackle to perfection. Even worse, he's still in possession and running towards your half with the ball! Where is your defence? There's only one player who isn't stranded upfield! He tries to challenge but the ball is squared to their winger who then has only your goalkeeper to beat . . .

Choose a frame number from the appropriate list below and check on the front flap to see whether the opposition score or not:

    If they're a RED team   *B4*   *C1*   *F3*
    If they're a BLUE team   *D3*   *F5*   *E2*
    If they're a GREEN team   *A3*   *D5*   *E4*
    If they're a YELLOW team *B5*   *E1*   *B2*
If they do score, go to 3. If not, go to 176.

At last you're out on the pitch and your players can relax! The pressure on them from the media in the three weeks since the draw has been enormous. Especially unsettling have been those newspaper reports that various league clubs have become interested in some of your players. Anyway, the only thing important now is the match ahead. You've already decided to start it positively and put the opposition under immediate pressure. Your flying winger, Scott Baker, has been playing the best football of his life in the previous rounds and so you must really utilise his talents. Although he usually plays on the right wing, he can be just as effective on the left. On which wing should you start him?

If right wing   go to 63
If left wing   go to 28

Your players seem to have kept their best football for the very end of the match. There are some superb touches in the last few minutes, every one of them being cheered on by your passionate fans. In fact, their roars are so loud that for a second no one realises that the final whistle has gone. It definitely has gone, though. This most emotional match of your lives is over!

Turn to your SCORE CARD and tot up the

*final score for this semifinal match. If you
won it, go to 47. If you drew it, go to 168. If you
lost it, go to 40.*

104

That was so nearly one of the best goals this national
stadium would ever have seen. Instead, it's probably
one of the best saves. How their goalie plucked it out of
the air like that, you'll never know! *Go to 207.*

105

What a goalkeeper! His first-ever game against league
opposition and he saves a penalty! This has given you
just the lift you need for the rest of the match. *Go to 50.*

106

Wow, what a difference was made by bringing on your
substitute forward! You've always known young Tim
Graham's potential, of course, but even *you* wouldn't
have expected the lad to see quite so much of the ball.
He suddenly plays a quick one-two with Dean Walsh,

who lays the ball back to him perfectly. Taking advantage of the tiring opposition, Tim races clear of all their defenders. What a great chance – only the goalkeeper to beat!

Choose a frame number from the appropriate list below and see whether Tim scores or not:

If playing RED team	*F4*	*D2*	*C5*
If playing BLUE team	*C2*	*A6*	*D4*
If playing GREEN team	*B3*	*A2*	*D1*
If playing YELLOW team	*E3*	*D6*	*E6*

If he does score, go to 155. If not, go to 2.

107

At last the big day of the semifinal arrives. This is the one you simply can't lose. It's said that losing a semifinal is the biggest heartache of them all! As you lead your team out on to the famous ground, you nervously glance round at each of the massive, packed stands. Even though this is a neutral venue, the opposition's supporters must outnumber yours by at least ten to one!
Go to 64.

You've lost. What absolute heartache! Your players all look distraught but they did you proud. They couldn't have worked harder. On the day the opposition were the better team, but you certainly weren't disgraced. Your fans were wonderful, too. It makes you determined to progress even further in the competition next time. You'll be back!

If you would like to compete for the Cup again, you must return to the start of its third round at Paragraph 1. Better luck next time!

109

The perfect penalty! Their goalkeeper went the right way but had no chance at all. Your fans are going wild with excitement. It's no more than your team deserved for that dazzling run of Scott's!

Record your goal on your SCORE CARD. Go next to 45.

110

Well, you can't really blame Scott for the lost opportunity. He struck the ball perfectly. It was that supposedly weak goalkeeper of theirs you should blame. His full-stretch dive was as good as any you've ever seen! *Go to 69.*

111

Now Scott has dropped back a little, that tricky winger of theirs has far less space. But Scott's talents are soon being missed up front – especially his ability to hold on to the ball. You are now under much more pressure from their other winger and midfield players; their crosses are absolutely raining in! The ball is desperately kicked clear, but back it comes again. This time their centre-forward hurls himself towards the near post and meets the ball with an excellent header . . .

Choose a frame number from the appropriate list below and see whether the opposition score or not:

If playing RED team	E1	D6	C3
If playing BLUE team	D4	E3	A1
If playing GREEN team	E6	C6	B4
If playing YELLOW team	A2	E6	D2

If they do score, go to 37. If not, go to 157.

112

Ten minutes of the match have now passed and your team's early nerves finally seem to have settled. Perhaps this is the right time to start testing the opposition's *defence*. The best option seems to try a few runs on the wing – then, if you're dispossessed, at least it won't lead to any immediate threat on your own goal. But which of your wingers should you urge to make the runs – Gary Weeks on the left or young Scott Baker on the right?

If Weeks   go to 148
If Baker   go to 101

113

Your fans groan in disappointment. In one of your non-league games that definitely would have been a goal. But these professional team goalies are of a totally different calibre. It was a quite remarkable leap for the ball. The goalie didn't even have to tip it over for a corner! *Go to 172*.

114

As the first half progresses, your opponents – as expected – get a stronger and stronger grip on the game. While they sweep down on your goal area time and time again, you haven't once managed to venture out of your own half! At last, though, Scott Baker manages to elude his marker and races down the wing. Although his centre is blocked, the ball ricochets out for a corner. You decide that you must make the most of this rare opportunity and bring as many players forward as possible for the kick. You'll leave just the one back. Should it be your left-back, Craig . . . or your sweeper, Duncan?

If left-back   go to 92
If sweeper   go to 184

115

No wonder the opposition's large army of fans are making so much noise. That goal was an absolute screamer, giving your goalie no chance whatever! You've got to give it to this league team: when they get possession, their passing is a joy to watch – and their finishing can be quite devastating!

Record your opponents' goal on your SCORE CARD. Go next to 54.

116

This is a good spell. Everyone is passing well and the ball is flowing nicely through midfield. At the moment it's *you* who's playing like the league team! Dean Walsh is receiving much more of the ball – and with one glorious pass he picks out Gary Weeks, who controls and then strikes the ball. It's goalbound . . .

Choose a frame number from the appropriate list below and see whether you score or not:

If playing RED team	*C3*	*B6*	*A2*
If playing BLUE team	*E1*	*D6*	*C4*
If playing GREEN team	*B4*	*E3*	*A1*
If playing YELLOW team	*C6*	*F5*	*D6*

If you do score, go to 135. If not, go to 181.

117

Oh, that wonderful crossbar! Your goalie was well and truly beaten but perhaps the chance was just a bit *too* easy for their striker. He hurls himself at the rebound to try to make amends. But your goalie now has the ball safely hugged to his chest. **Go to 174.**

118

A signal from your bench tells you that there are now only fifteen minutes of the match left. You're determined to push out of defence and have a go during these final stages. You must make the most of this once-in-a-lifetime opportunity! Your best option must surely be somehow to involve Scott Baker. He's been your outstanding player throughout the competition. Should you allow him a free rein to play wherever he wants for the remainder of the match? Or will he be more effective kept on the right wing?

> *If give him free rein*   **go to 189**
> *If leave him on wing*   **go to 97**

The replay on your opponents' ground proves as scrappy as the original match was exciting – all 120 minutes of it! The final result after extra time stands at 1–1; both goals being a result of defensive mistakes rather than any particular skill. So now it's all down to the dreaded penalties! *Go to 26.*

This is easily the best team you've met in the Cup so far. The first fifteen minutes are played at such a pace that you barely have time to draw breath. Their number eight is well contained – he's hardly had a kick. But their ex-international winger is running rampant. Just as you're about to instruct some changes to deal with him, he receives a perfect pass and hares towards the goal line. When he reaches it he looks as if he's going to cross, but then he suddenly dribbles round the next defender. With a glorious chip to the far post he picks out one of their strikers who has plenty of time to pick his spot.

Choose a frame number from the appropriate list below and see whether your opponents score or not:

If they're a RED team	B3	A1	E1
If they're a BLUE team	C5	E6	C3
If they're a GREEN team	C2	C6	D2

If they score, go to 12. If they don't, go to 137.

121

What a fantastic acrobatic save! It's cost you a corner, though, and your defence is still one man short. You frantically wave everyone back, hoping to crowd the opposition out. It wasn't necessary, however. Just as their corner-taker makes contact with the ball, the wind suddenly drops and it drifts harmlessly behind the goal. There's more good news for you. Duncan is now ready to come back on! *Go to 81.*

122

You sink to the turf in a mixture of exhaustion and total anguish. The dejection is terrible – all of your players are completely heartbroken. You somehow force yourself to your feet, though, and slowly gather them for a lap of honour. To begin with it's a dispirited trudge, but there's not one spectator who isn't on his feet to applaud your incredible achievement. You soon start to feel encouraged to try again . . .

If you would like to compete for the Cup

again, you must return to the start of the third round at Paragraph 1. With the experience you've gained, and perhaps just a little more luck, you might even win it next time!

123

You're sure even your opponents' fans are cheering your goalie's save. It was quite outstanding: he had to leap from one side of the goal to the other. You're lucky you didn't have to pay for that bad decision of yours about the wall. It left your goalie completely unprotected! *Go to 55*.

124

Some of your players are jumping up and down with excitement while others just sink to their knees with emotion. You've done it again! That's another league team beaten! Even after two laps of honour no one wants to leave the pitch. Surely you can never have a greater day than this one. Yes, you can – if you go right through to win the Final! *Go to 156*.

125

A few minutes into the second half, your left-back tries his first run. He hares down the wing into an empty area. He has an opportunity to cross but he decides to try to get even closer to the goal line to create an even

better chance. But it means skipping past a defender –
and the defender tackles him brilliantly, leaving him
sprawling on the ground! There's now a break on for
the opposition. A long ball from that defender releases
his winger deep into your half. The winger crosses
perfectly to one of his strikers, who immediately shoots
at goal before any of your defenders can race across to
tackle him . . .

Choose a frame number from the appropriate
list below and see whether your opponents'
striker scores or not:
If they're a RED team	A5	E4	D1
If they're a BLUE team	A1	F6	D2
If they're a GREEN team	E6	D3	C6

If he does score, go to 27. If not, go to 140.

126

What a volley! How did he do it from that angle? From
the moment it left his foot the ball was in. Thank
goodness the cameras are here. Even if you don't win

the Cup, you've scored the goal of the competition. Poor Gary – he's buried under a pile of delirious players!

Record your goal on your SCORE CARD. Go next to 192.

127

There are now less than ten minutes to go to half-time and you wonder whether you should take a risk and go all-out for goal. After all, you are the home side! So while there's a break in the play, you consider whether you wave midfielder Dean Walsh forward to join the strikers.

If yes   go to 9
If no   go to 87

128

No matter how well you've done to get this far, the disappointment in losing is devastating. It's a hundred times worse than you imagined! But the fact remains that you played extremely well and didn't let anyone down. And it seems that the whole town turned up to watch your efforts. At least you've found a whole new lot of supporters for your next attempt at the competition!

If you would like to compete for the Cup again, you must return to the start of its third round at Paragraph 1. With the experience you've gained, and perhaps with just a little more luck, you might get even further next time!

129

You bury your face in your hands as an elated roar breaks all round you. The opposition has gone 1–0 up already! Unless your team quickly overcomes these nerves and settles down, this could be an absolute rout. Far from your Cup run ending in glory, it could end in complete humiliation!

Record the opposition's goal on your SCORE CARD. Go next to 112.

130

These long through-balls to Andy's feet prove a good tactic. Although he's all on his own up there, he's able to use his great strength to hold on to the ball until support arrives. This is just what he does after a lovely ball through to him from Duncan Hill, your number four. The support haring up to him is none other than yourself! Collecting Andy's perfectly weighted pass in your stride, you immediately knock it out towards Gary Weeks. Gary is equally quick, instantly centring the ball before a defender's tackle comes in. Having sprinted forward, Andy leaps like a salmon to head the ball towards goal . . .

Choose a frame number from the appropriate list below and see whether Andy scores or not:
If playing RED team	E1	D2	A1
If playing BLUE team	D4	B4	D6
If playing GREEN team	F5	A2	E6

If Andy does score, go to 93. If not, go to 42.

131

The bend on the ball was incredible: it looked as if it was going well wide at first. What a fantastic goal!

Add a goal for your team to your SCORE CARD, then go to 50.

132

If their striker had tried to place it rather than blast it, your goalie surely wouldn't have got anywhere near. As it is, he's a sore-fingered hero! *Go to 22*.

133

The referee seems to be awarding a lot of free kicks.
And here's another one – for one of your strikers is
suddenly pulled down by his marker and the referee
immediately blows his whistle. Unfortunately, it's too
far out for a direct shot. But perhaps you can score from
it if you push forward Darren Palmer, your tall central
defender, into their penalty area. It's a bit of a risk,
though, because they have speedy players who can
break quickly and Darren will no longer be there to
help out!

If push Darren forward   *go to 195*
If leave him back   *go to 53*

134

Now the game has started you're not so sure it was such
a good idea to have the wind behind you at the outset.
Your defenders and midfield players can't gauge it

properly. They're constantly over-hitting the ball when trying to find your strikers. Your opponents are craftily picking up these loose balls and building dangerous counter-attacks with short passes. One such move ends in a high punt into your goalmouth. It's just perfect for the head of their striker . . .

Choose a frame number from the appropriate list below and see whether your opponents score or not:
    If they're a RED team   C2   D6   F3
    If they're a BLUE team   B3   A2   D5
If they score, go to 209. If they don't, go to 117.

135

Your fans are jumping up and down with delight. What a great shot and what a time for Gary to score the best goal of his career! The cameras are here as well so the whole country will see it!

Record your goal on your SCORE CARD. Go next to 21.

136

What a brilliant touch on to the post from their keeper! Their full back shows equal brilliance, kicking the ball over his head to clear it upfield. It's now at the feet of one of their forwards. The only defender you kept back dives in desperately but he completely misses the ball. Now their forward is bearing down on your goal! Your goalie quickly moves out to meet him but the forward skips round him and runs the ball into an empty net. What a disaster! They've scored with only seconds left to play. In fact, there isn't even that. A moment after the restart, the final whistle goes! *Go to 10*.

137

What a great reflex save from your goalie! Although he could only palm it back into play, one of your defenders quickly hooks the loose ball out of danger, thumping it towards the halfway line. That international winger of theirs should obviously have been marked more closely. But at least you just about got away with this tactical error! *Go to 186*.

138

It was a fantastic shot . . . but an even better save! How on earth did your keeper get his hands to it so he could push it against the post? And how did he then manage to beat everyone to the rebound? It was pure athleticism from him! *Go to 45*.

Although you say it yourself, you're doing a superb marking job on their star midfielder. What you're particularly pleased about is that you're not wasting Dean's special talents. He's continuing to operate in the part of the field that he likes best, just behind the strikers. And he's been operating there brilliantly for the last few minutes, distributing one exquisite pass after another. One ball from him completely splits the defence to find Gary Weeks on his own. All he has to do is keep a cool head to beat the goalie . . .

Choose a frame number from the appropriate list below and see whether Gary scores or not:
If playing RED team   E4   F1   B6
If playing BLUE team   C4   B6   D3
If he does score, go to 23. If not, go to 99.

140
Thank heavens for your goalie's great save. That would have been a terrible goal to give away. You can do without giving your superior opponents gift chances like that! *Go to 198.*

Your fans are ecstatic. It was a tremendous goal, floated beautifully over their goalie. He must be livid with himself for coming so far off his line. So it's 1–0 to you already. Could you possibly win this match as well?

Record your team's goal on your SCORE CARD. Go next to 172.

After the longest three weeks you can remember, your fourth-round match is at last about to begin. The referee beckons you and the opposition's captain to the centre for the toss. You choose heads. Heads it is. Well, at least you've won something today! Which end should you play towards? This is a big decision. Your ground isn't *league* standard, of course. The surface is quite awful in places – especially with all this rain that's lashing down. In fact, the penalty area at one end is a complete mudbath! Should you defend that bad end in

the first half, or should you make *them* defend it and try
to take advantage of their early mistakes?

> **If defend bad end**   **go to 61**
> **If make them defend it**   **go to 200**

143

Your fans behind the goal reacted slowly – they all
thought Dean's shot was going wide. But it suddenly
swerved at the last moment and just scraped inside the
post. It was struck beautifully, just like the Brazilians do
it. A magnificent free kick!

***Record your team's goal on your SCORE
CARD. Go next to 206.***

144

You shouldn't have listened to your right-back's pleas!
His weakened ankle is tested almost immediately, the
opposition's winger running straight at him. Your

defender simply can't turn fast enough and his attacker rounds him with ease. The winger now cuts in towards goal, slipping the ball to one of his forwards who surely has the easiest scoring chance of the match yet . . .

Choose a frame number from the list below and see whether your opponents score or not:

D6   B2   C5

If your opponents do score, go to 78. If they don't, go to 51.

145

Andy's header was absolutely ferocious but your opponents' international goalie was more than equal to it. No disrespect, but you're sure your own goalie couldn't pull off a tremendous save like that. You can only hope that he doesn't have to! *Go to 174.*

146

There's now such a sustained onslaught from the opposition that all you can do is pray for the half-time whistle to be blown. It's still a good ten minutes away, though. Their winger is on *yet another* of his lethal runs and releases their striker into your penalty area. Fortunately, Duncan makes an excellently-timed tackle. At least, you thought it was excellently-timed . . . but the referee immediately awards a penalty! Your goalie looks at you in desperation, wanting to know what he should do. You know that their penalty-taker usually strikes to the right. So what should you tell your goalie? Should he dive in that direction as soon as the ball is kicked, or just stand his ground?

If dive   **go to 77**
If stay still   **go to 194**

147

You realised that wall was a bad mistake of yours even before the ball had reached the net! You must have been mad putting only three men in it against a team of free-kick specialists like this! You must remember that you're playing against some of the best players in the country now, not your average Sunday-league team!

Record your opponents' goal on your SCORE CARD. Go next to 55.

148

Gary immediately responds to the forward wave of your arm and attempts a run with the ball. His first run is foiled by a swift and precise tackle but on the second he neatly skips over this same defender. He then outpaces two other defenders and sends over a cross worthy of any Premier League winger! Unfortunately, your striker, Andy Jones, doesn't meet it very cleanly. The ball spins off his boot towards the crossbar. But it fortuitously comes back right at his feet. All he has to do is stroke it past the goalie . . .

Choose a frame number from the appropriate list below and check on the front flap to see whether Andy scores or not:

If playing RED team	*C3*	*B6*	*A5*
If playing BLUE team	*D3*	*F6*	*A1*
If playing GREEN team	*C1*	*C4*	*F2*
If playing YELLOW team	*C6*	*D3*	*E4*

If he does score, go to 35. If not, go to 173.

149

Scott is certainly seeing much more of the ball now and he's making some good runs. But his high crosses are posing few problems for the opposition. Crosses like these might work against non-league teams but these professional players have been far too well coached. They're so organised in the air . . . big Andy is being out-jumped every time! *Go to 103.*

150

That was quite an incredible stretch from your goalie –
but you can't applaud it yet. The ball's still in play! One
of the opposition's forwards merely scoops the loose
ball over the bar. The moment he does so, you all
clamour round your goalie, slapping him on the back.
Without that brilliant save of his you would surely have
been out of the game! *Go to 31*.

151

You'd hoped that with the advantage of home ground
you'd be able to *win* the return match. But it proves just
as tight as the first one. Even after extra time there's
nothing to separate the teams. So it's penalties to decide
who goes through! The opposition put each penalty
away well but you're able to match them strike for
strike. They're now ahead again, though: 5–4. If you
don't score from this final penalty, out you go! Poor
Craig James looks a bag of nerves as he prepares for this
terrible responsibility. The only advice you can give

him is to decide which way to shoot, and *go for it*! Then you can no longer bear to look . . .

Choose a frame number from the appropriate list below and see whether Craig scores or not from this penalty:

If playing RED team	*F5*	*A6*	*E2*
If playing BLUE team	*B5*	*D6*	*E1*
If playing GREEN team	*A2*	*D1*	*B4*
If playing YELLOW team	*E3*	*A3*	*F5*

If Craig does score, go to 57. If not, go to 108.

152

You join in all the wild applause for your goalie, showing your admiration for his great save. It's a double relief for you. If that deflected ball had gone in, not only might it well have lost your team the match but it would surely have given you nightmares for ever after. You still can't be certain that it wasn't *your* head that the ball came off! **Go to 207**.

153

Up goes the linesman's flag for the third time, much to your relief – and your opponents' displeasure! The offside trap's working so far. While the opposition are arguing with the linesman, your side takes a quick free kick and sends Scott Baker away down the right wing. The break is on and Scott wastes no time in delivering a first-time cross. Opposition defenders are trying to get back while your forwards are racing in. Who will get there first? It's Matt Coles, your striker, with a clear sight of goal!

Choose a frame number from the appropriate list below and see whether he scores or not:

If playing RED team	*F3*	*C5*	*A6*
If playing BLUE team	*E1*	*C2*	*D1*
If playing GREEN team	*D5*	*F5*	*B3*
If playing YELLOW team	*B4*	*B2*	*E1*

If he does score, go to 131. If not, go to 36.

154

The presentation seems to last for ever. Oh, why don't they just get the match started before this huge, intimidating arena makes you run right back into the tunnel? But you try to take your mind off all the banners and balloons, the tier after tier of chanting spectators, and work out your final plans for this match. Your opponents are the top team in the country. They've just won the Premier League and are going for that elusive double. You must choose very carefully the system of play you adopt. Should it be 4–3–3, with three players for both midfield and attack? Or 4–2–4, with a smaller midfield but an extra man up front?

If a 4–2–4 system go to 175
If a 4–3–3 system go to 29

155

What a shot! Just when you thought Tim might try to run at the goalie, he takes everyone by surprise with a blistering thunderbolt. It must have been twenty-five yards at least! What a super sub!

Record your goal on your SCORE CARD. Go next to 193.

156

The whole town is now hooked by the magic of the Cup, eagerly awaiting the draw for the fifth round. On the day of the draw, you push your way through a mass of reporters to join the rest of the team at your training ground. At this stage, not only are there no other non-league teams left, there aren't many from the lower leagues either! So you can't hope for an easy opponent any longer. There aren't any!

To find out who you're playing against in the

fifth round, pick one of these draw numbers: **22** **6** **13** **26** **24** *and then look up that number in the DRAW LIST on the front flap of the book. Be sure to remember this team's name! Now go to 82.*

157
Great reflexes! Your goalie just did enough to push the ball on to the far post. And, fortunately, one of your defenders was first to get to the rebound, quickly thumping the ball upfield. *Go to 127.*

158
You're winning one throw-in after another and Dean's efforts are as long and accurate as ever. However, there simply isn't enough height in the box to take advantage of them. Perhaps you should have moved Darren Palmer up after all! At least the centre of your defence is holding strong, though. The opposition simply can't find a way through. *Go to 72.*

The opposition's tall defenders seem to have little difficulty coping with your long-balls. Your forwards are barely getting a touch and all this tactic means is that you keep losing possession! Suddenly, their winger breaks free with the ball. Just when you're expecting a cross, he cuts inside and your full back is left tackling empty space. As your goalie comes out to attempt a block, the winger slips the ball to his number eight who has come running in alongside him. He must surely score!

Choose a frame number from the appropriate list below and see whether the opposition score or not:

If they're a RED team	F6	A3	C1
If they're a BLUE team	D3	A5	B2
If they're a GREEN team	F2	B5	E4
If they're a YELLOW team	C1	F3	E2

If the opposition do score, go to 18. If they don't, go to 39.

Only four minutes left and Andy's done it – he's got the breakthrough! Although their goalie attempted a brilliant backward spin, the chip was always too clever for him and he couldn't quite reach it. Straight from the restart, your opponents throw everyone forward in desperation. Barely able to watch, your fans start howling for the final whistle to be blown. These are the longest few minutes of your life. Finally, though, the shrill sound of the whistle pierces the night air . . . *Go to 90.*

161

Why on earth has the linesman raised his flag? That was surely a perfect goal from Andy! Still, you can't argue with the officials. The linesman must have thought that your striker did some pushing! *Go to 198.*

162

Phew, that was certainly a risk by your keeper, aiming to prevent not just the goal but also any resultant corner! Your nerves would have been easier if he had just played safe and fisted the ball away. Still, he managed to bring it off. A perfectly-timed diving clasp! *Go to 54.*

163

After a jig of celebration, Scott runs across to your fans. They're deliriously chanting his name. Well, it was a brilliant strike after all. Even the best goalie in the land wouldn't have been able to stop that one!

Record your team's goal on your SCORE CARD. Go next to 62.

Right from the kick-off, your players have real difficulty clearing the ball in this strong wind. But the wind creates even greater problems for your opponents. Every time they punt the ball forward, they over-kick it so it carries straight through to your goalie. They then try hitting the ball shorter but one ball is far too short and is picked up by Gary Weeks on the wing. He runs determinedly at the goal line. Although he's unable to centre, he wins a corner. Taking the kick himself, he finds big Andy's head perfectly . . .

Choose a frame number from the appropriate list below and see whether Andy scores or not:
> *If playing RED team*   F4   C3   A2
> *If playing BLUE team*   A6   C6   B3
If he does score, go to 98. If not, go to 145.

The referee keeps delaying their free kick, insisting that your wall should be further back. At last he blows the whistle. It's the fiercest-struck ball you've ever seen, and it goes straight into Darren Palmer's stomach! Your decision about the wall seems to have been the right one. Still, try telling poor Darren that! *Go to 55*.

166

The opposition's fans are going delirious. YOU are absolutely livid, though. There's no doubt that that chip was measured beautifully, but what was your goalie doing so far out? And what a terrible corner that was from Scott. His carelessness directly turned a goal-scoring opportunity for you into one for them!

Record your opponents' goal on your SCORE CARD. Go next to 146.

167

That instinctive save seems to bring the opposition to life all of a sudden. They start a flurry of attacks. You just about deal with one after another but then, in the very last seconds, a particularly wicked cross causes absolute panic in your penalty area. You all look at each other in disbelief as an opponent smashes the loose ball into the back of the net. Before there's even time for their fans to cheer the goal, the final whistle goes. *Go next to 122*.

168

There's no replay at this semifinal stage – it's straight into extra time. This is a real worry for you. Your players obviously won't be as fit as the professionally-trained opposition. You only hope that they can somehow find the stamina to survive! The first period of extra time, however, seems to pass in a flash. There isn't a single real chance for either side. *Go to 95*.

169

Duncan has been outstanding in every round of the Cup. But he's really got his hands full now. He's suddenly got *two* tall strikers to deal with – and they're being supplied by lots of accurate crosses as well! The lanky substitute completely outjumps Duncan for one of these crosses, his forehead guiding it powerfully towards goal . . .

Choose a frame number from the appropriate list below to see whether your opponents score or not:
   If they're a RED team   *A6*   *C5*   *E3*
   If they're a BLUE team   *C2*   *D1*   *F4*
   If they're a GREEN team   *A6*   *F4*   *A2*
If they do score, go to 44. If not, go to 20.

170

You just can't believe you're out of the Cup at last. The pain of getting this close to the semis and then losing is simply unbearable. But you played your best and can have no complaints. You also won many friends on the way. A lot of your players are now household names. So you are determined to be back again and to do even better next time.

If you would like to compete for the Cup

again, you must return to the start of the third round at Paragraph 1. With the experience you've gained, and perhaps just a little more luck, you might go even further next time!

171

Everything seems to be a complete blur for the next five minutes. As if in a trance, you feel hands coming at you from all directions, then one of these hands eventually guides you to some steps. You wobble up these steps, climbing through a sea of ecstatic faces. Someone hugs you, someone pats you on the back, someone ties his scarf around your neck. There are cheers and shouts everywhere. Then you become aware that someone's handing you something large and shiny. The whole stadium seems to erupt as you instinctively raise this heavy object high above your head. Your little non-league team has done the impossible. *It's won the Cup!*

The first half is approaching the midway mark now but Andy Jones has barely touched the ball. Your big striker has been one of the real stars of your team in previous rounds – but this time he simply hasn't been allowed to get into the game. You realise that you've got to involve him more if you are to be sure of winning this match. But what sort of service should you supply to him? Should they be high balls to make the most of his heading ability, or would he do better with balls to his feet?

If high balls   *go to 79*
If balls to his feet   *go to 130*

How you feel for poor Andy! Only the goalie to beat and he hits it virtually straight at him. No wonder there's so much derision from the home stands! Still, you know Andy is a far better striker of the ball than that. As long as he doesn't let this bad miss undermine his confidence, you're sure he can have the last laugh over the home fans. *Go to 133*.

For the last quarter of an hour, your opponents have been absolutely dominating the match. Only a series of desperate last-minute tackles have kept them out. One fiercely-contested cross leaves Duncan Hill, your sweeper, rolling on the ground with a head wound. The referee says he must go off the field of play for treatment. He's not likely to be back on again for a good ten minutes. You don't want to use a substitute this early in the game – and so who should you move to take Duncan's place? The most suitable candidates are either your left-back . . . or yourself!

If left-back   go to 38
If yourself   go to 89

175

Playing against this 4–2–4 system you've imposed – with only two of your players in the middle – the opposition's international midfield are soon creating a whole host of good chances for their forwards. *Your* forwards, though, have been reduced to little more than spectators! You're just about to signal to Gary Weeks to drop back a bit to help out the midfield, when a neat passing movement by the opposition creates the best chance yet for their number nine. Duncan Hill tries to put in a tackle but it's too late. Their striker has already let loose with the ball . . .

Choose a frame number from the list below and see whether your opponents score or not:

E1   F6   B2

If they do score, go to 76. If not, go to 190.

176

What a let off! Thank goodness their forward didn't steady himself before shooting. He didn't seem to realise just how much time he had. You can't afford to give the ball away so easily to a team as good as this. *Go to 133.*

177

It was a good try. But one or two of your players feel Gary should have controlled it instead of shooting first time – and they're letting him know it! *Go to 192.*

Scott responds to the better service he's getting with several fine, weaving runs down the wing. His low, hard crosses are causing all sorts of trouble, even for these quality defenders. They're so hard to read! One particularly good run takes him right to the goal line. It's a great position. After a quick glance up, he fires the ball along the ground. The ball ricochets off one defender to land right in Dean Walsh's path. Dean hits it first time for goal . . .

Choose a frame number from the appropriate list below and see whether Dean scores or not:
    If playing RED team   *F6   B2   D5*
    If playing BLUE team   *F3   A5   B2*
If you do score, go to 25. If you don't, go to 74.

179

Although your right-back was very upset as he hobbled off the field – who wants to quit a Cup Final? – you're sure you've made the right decision. The substitute settles in very quickly and makes a couple of vital interceptions. You very much doubt that your injured player would have been able to move across that fast. ***Go to 118.***

180

The extra defender on him means that their winger's runs have now been more or less snuffed out. Indeed, it's your own winger, Scott, who's now creating the most mischief. How wise of you to have left him forward! ***Go to 127.***

181

Gary puts his head in his hands. How could he not have scored? He simply can't believe it! Against any other keeper that would surely have been a goal. It was quite an incredible save! ***Go to 21.***

182

After a month of uncontained excitement in your little town, the big day at last arrives. The last few weeks have seemed one long dream. The interviews have been almost non-stop: with television, newspapers and magazines. You've had approaches from all sorts of big sponsors. You've even made a record which is riding high in the charts. A good job big Andy Jones can head a ball much better than he can sing! But that's all over now. The coach is ready to take you from your hotel to the national stadium. The most important ninety minutes of your lives is just hours away . . . *Go to 86*.

183

As the ball thumps the back of the net, Scott is already running towards your small band of supporters to celebrate. What a classic breakaway goal! It perfectly justified your decision to leave Andy up front. If you hadn't, it could even have been the *opposition* who are celebrating now!

Record your team's goal on your SCORE CARD. Go next to 69.

184

Scott powers the corner-kick across the face of the goal but one of their defenders coolly hooks it clear to the halfway line. The only players anywhere near it are Duncan and the opposition's number nine. Being so fast, Duncan easily reaches the ball first and lofts it straight back deep into their half. It's flicked down by big Andy Jones into the path of your sturdy left-back. He shoots first time through the crowded penalty area . . .

Choose a frame number from the list below and see whether he scores or not:

F1   D3   B6

If your left-back does score, go to 30. If he doesn't, go to 100.

185

That header of yours was so desperately close! How disappointing! Still, although the ball didn't quite go in, it was a good example to set for the rest of the lads. It should really encourage them! *Go to 50.*

186

As the match approaches the midway mark of the first half, there's another period of heavy pressure from your opponents. One of their midfielders suddenly has a clear run on goal. Fortunately, one of your defenders catches up with him in time and makes a saving tackle just on the edge of the area. The referee calls your player over and holds a yellow card in the air. He's booked him! Their midfielder was obviously injured by the crunching tackle . . . for very soon a substitute is brought on – a forward. Now they have *four* strikers! Should you pull someone back to reinforce your defence or just keep things as they are?

If order someone back   go to 19
If stick with formation   go to 70

187

What a class header that was. Most forwards would have just hit it as hard as possible, but this one was beautiful to watch. At least, it would have been if it wasn't against *you*! So Duncan's injury has cost you dearly. What a relief that he's now ready to come back on.

Record your opponents' goal on your SCORE CARD. Go next to 81.

You have to admit that was a well-worked goal. Good running, an accurate pass, and a great final shot. This team is even better than you were expecting – in a totally different class, really. Your fans seem to realise it too. There are just stunned faces staring back at you from their stand!

Record your opponents' goal on your SCORE CARD. Go next to 210.

Scott has been tightly marked up to this stage of the game. But now, because he's running freely between midfield and attack, the opposition are finding him much more of a handful. He's picked up the ball *again*, and is moving forward into a space. With a drop of the shoulder he sends the first opposition defender the wrong way. Then he flicks the ball to the right of the next defender, brilliantly running round to his other side to collect it again. After another quick touch, he sends the ball flying towards the top corner of the goal . . .

Choose a frame number from the list below and see whether Scott scores or not:

C3   F5   C6

If Scott does score, go to 32. If he doesn't, go to 104.

190

What a let off! If that ball had been a fraction lower –
and if it hadn't luckily rebounded into your goalie's
arm! – it would have been disaster for you. Going down
this early in a Cup Final, especially against a quality
team like this, would probably have been impossible to
recover from. *Go to 114*.

191

Now just about everyone in your town is wearing your
team colours. They can hardly believe that a tiny non-
league club like theirs has made it all the way to the
Cup's quarter-final! You're very relaxed about who
you're to be drawn against next – you now really believe
you can beat almost anyone! In fact, *yours* is the team
that no one wants to be drawn against. The seven other
teams left in the competition regard you as a dangerous
unknown quantity! The televised draw begins . . . and
yours is the first team out of the bag. You've got a home

tie! All the other managers will be quaking in their boots as the name of your opponent is now lifted from the bag . . .

To find out who this opponent is to be, pick one of these draw numbers: ⑪ ⑨ ㉑ ㉓ ④ ⑭ ⑯ *and then look up that number in the DRAW LIST on the front flap of the book. Be sure to remember this team's name. Now go to 102.*

192

It's soon half-time, and what a difference this interval makes. The moment the match restarts, the opposition switch to all-out attack. You must do something quickly. You can think of only two options. Do you push upfield and try to trap them offside, or do you defend more deeply and bring more players back to weather the storm?

Try to trap them   **go to 153**
Defend more deeply   **go to 4**

Players on both sides are by now so weary that the passing has become quite awful! When will the referee blow the whistle? It seems he's had it in his mouth for at least five minutes! But, at last, he does blow . . .

Turn to your SCORE CARD and tot up the final score for this third-round match. If you won it, go to 73. If you drew it, go to 151. If you lost it, go to 108.

194

Following your instructions, your keeper stands still and tall in his goalmouth. But as their penalty-taker runs up to the spot in the deathly silence, you realise you gave the wrong advice. *He's aiming well to the right!* Unless your goalie realises this too, and quickly changes his intentions, it's going to be a certain goal . . .

Choose a frame number from the list below and see whether your opponents score or not:

F6   B4   D2

If they do score, go to 49. If not, go to 150.

There's a lot of jostling for position in the opposition's
packed penalty area. Darren has his hands in the air
calling for the ball as you yourself prepare to take the
free kick. Darren's presence has certainly unnerved the
opposition! As the ball comes in, he darts to the near
post taking three of their defenders with him. They're
determined he won't score! All Darren can manage is
the merest flick which takes the ball right to the other
side of the penalty area. It's not an easy chance, but one
of your strikers, Gary Weeks, is going to hit it first
time . . .

*Choose a frame number from the appropriate
list below and see whether Gary scores or not:*
If playing RED team	B2	E3	A1
If playing BLUE team	F3	C2	D6
If playing GREEN team	B3	A2	C6
If playing YELLOW team	D5	B3	C5

*If Gary does score go to 126. If he doesn't, go
to 177.*

196

Their player hadn't taken much of a run-up but he'd
placed that penalty perfectly! A big final effort is now
needed if you're going to make the next round . . .

***Record the opposition's goal on your SCORE
CARD. Go next to 50.***

What a glorious goal from Dean. It was a great idea to push him upfield. That will keep your fans warm at half-time!

Record your goal on your SCORE CARD. Go next to 203.

198

Only fifteen minutes to go now and your players are noticeably tiring. Gaps are appearing everywhere on the pitch and the opposition is exploiting them much better than you are. A quick high cross from the wing catches your left-back, Craig James, out of position. Without thinking, he puts his hand in the air to intercept the ball. He realises his mistake straight away . . . he's already had one booking in this match and so for this second offence he'll be sent off! What are you going to do? Your defence is now one man short! Should you pull back big Andy Jones to replace Craig in defence?

Or should you leave Andy up front to try to keep the play at the other end of the pitch?

If pull Andy back   **go to 91**
If keep him up front   **go to 24**

199

Your stadium has never heard a noise like it. Only five minutes to go now and you've scored! And what a great goal it was from big Andy, too – a textbook header, smashed downwards towards the goal line!

Record your team's goal on your SCORE CARD. Go next to 72.

200

It's only ten minutes into the match and already your terrible pitch is giving you a big advantage. Although your opponents are playing well through midfield, with sweet passing movements, their defenders can hardly stand up in that treacherous penalty area! Andy Jones, your striker, is never happier than in these muddy conditions. He is constantly calling for the ball and, happily, Gary Weeks keeps crossing it to him from the left. Although your winger's third crossed ball doesn't quite reach him, stopping dead in the mud, Andy is the fastest to react to the situation. He's seen this happen so many times before! He beats all their defenders to the ball and immediately chips it towards the corner of the goal.

Choose a frame number from the appropriate list below and see whether you score or not:

If playing RED team	*A6*	*C5*	*D2*
If playing BLUE team	*E6*	*B4*	*C2*
If playing GREEN team	*F5*	*B3*	*D1*
If playing YELLOW team	*E1*	*F4*	*C5*

If you score, go to 7. If you don't, go to 56.

201

After failing to take full advantage of the home tie, you've been very worried about this replay. But the conditions are so much better on the opposition's ground and you perhaps make even more of them than they do. Nevertheless, after ninety minutes it's still 0–0 and this deadlock continues deep into extra time. It looks like going to penalties! To avoid this terrible situation, you decide really to put the pressure on for the last few seconds of the game. Scott Baker wins a corner on the right and you wave all your defenders except one into their goalmouth. Scott swerves the corner-kick well clear of their goalie towards where you're lurking at the far post. You meet the ball with your instep. If this goes in, you're surely through to the next round . . .

Choose a frame number from the appropriate list below and see whether you score or not:

If playing RED team	E6	A5	D4
If playing BLUE team	E4	D2	F6
If playing GREEN team	F2	C1	E6
If playing YELLOW team	D3	F6	D2

If you do score, go to 124. If not, go to 136.

202

It proves an effective tactic to put an extra marker on their winger. You are just about able to cope with the ex-international now! Although he frequently manages to skip round one tackle, you always have someone else there to provide some cover. As for their record-signing number eight, you and the other central defender are just about able to handle him without any assistance. It looks as if you made the right choice about the extra marker! *Go to 186*.

203

The whistle is now blown for half-time and during the interval you consider how best to approach the rest of the game. The pitch is likely to become even worse in the second half! So should you continue playing through midfield . . . or just completely bypass the midfield, lobbing long-balls straight to your strikers. It's nearly time to go out for the second half. What will your decision be?

If play through midfield   go to 116
If bypass midfield   go to 159

204

What a save! It wasn't that it was a bad penalty – Dean struck it well enough – but their keeper guessed the right way and just got both hands to it. *Go to 45*.

205

What cruel luck! The ball hit the crossbar and bounced straight back into the goalie's arms! This terrible luck completely unbalances your team. Straight away, the opposition turn defence into attack. A dangerous cross comes into your penalty area and your goalie does well to punch it clear. But it's immediately volleyed straight back at him. It's a goal! You're still reeling from the injustice of it all when the referee blows the final whistle. *Go to 128*.

206

As the match enters its last quarter of an hour, no one can doubt that your team's had the best of the play in this half. Listen to your fans singing their hearts out!

Your opponents at last decide to do something about it and their manager makes a substitution. On to the pitch runs a very tall striker. How do you deal with this new threat? Your defence is already fully occupied with the opposition's other forwards. So do you instruct your sweeper, Duncan Hill, to look after this lanky substitute, or pull big Andy Jones back from attack?

If give job to Duncan   **go to 169**
If pull back Andy   **go to 33**

207

The stadium starts to hum with tension, telling you that there are now very few minutes to go. At one end, the fans are praying for as much injury time as possible – at the other, they're screaming for the referee's whistle! You hope your players won't be affected by this. They must keep their concentration right to the final second. As you suddenly find yourself with the ball, you desperately wave everyone forward. But several of your players have bad cramp and can hardly move.

You decide to try to take the ball upfield yourself, advancing much further than you'd hoped. But then you realise why. Drowned out by the tumultuous noise all round you was the final whistle!

Turn to your SCORE CARD and tot up the final score for this match. If you won it, go to 171. If you drew it, go to 94. If you lost it, go to 122.

208

It seems that the day of your third-round match will never come . . . but at last you're having your pre-match talk with your players. It's in a dressing-room far more luxurious than your own – that's one advantage, you suppose, of having been drawn away. But the disadvantage is the huge and deafening support for your opponents in the stands above you. As you all nervously make your way to the tunnel, you tell your players to try to ignore this and just to concentrate on the team's tactics. But what should these be for the first part of the match? Should you try and completely surprise the opposition by going for all-out attack? Or should you play much more cautiously, making sure that you just contain the opposition to begin with?

If all-out attack   ***go to 52***
If play a containing game   ***go to 34***

209

Only ten minutes into the Cup semifinal and you're already one goal down! At least there's plenty of time for you to find the equaliser. On the other hand, there's plenty of time for the opposition to add to that score. You hope it's not going to be a rout!

Record your opponents' goal on your SCORE CARD. Go next to 174.

With just twenty minutes of the match left now, you decide to go for all-out attack. It's a huge risk, of course – but this *is* the semifinal of the Cup and you'll probably never get this far again. You really want to make that final and write yourself into the history books! Scott Baker has been very quiet in this half so far, so you signal to your players that they should feed him more. You'd better signal instructions to Scott himself as well so he knows what sort of crosses you want from him. Should he hit them low and hard – or lob them up?

If prefer low crosses   *go to 178*
If prefer high crosses   *go to 149*

Collect all six titles in this series:

And have you also read Stephen Thraves'
Super Adventure Game Books
with separate cards and special dice?